# CRACK.
# CHIRP. CHIRP.

## How to Help Our Animal Friends

## By Paula Feuerstein

## Illustrated by Daniel Traynor

# CRACKLE. CHIRP. CHIRP.

## How to Help Our Animal Friends

By Paula Feuerstein
Cover and Illustrations by Daniel Traynor
Edited by Mark H. Newhouse

AimHi Press
Orlando, Florida
AimHiPress.com
2019, Paula Feuerstein

Names: Feuerstein, Paula. | Traynor, Daniel, illustrator. | Newhouse, Mark, Editor.
Title: Crackle. Chirp. Chirp.: How to Help Our Animal Friends / by Estella Shivers
Description: Orlando, FL :AimHi Press, 2019. | Summary: When a baby bird is
caught in a plastic bag on a tree branch, Luna and her friends are on a mission
to save him!
Identifiers: LCCN 2019940825 (print) | ISBN 978-1-945493-16-4 (paperback)
Subjects: CYAC: Environment. | Ecology. |Animals. | Wildlife. | Planet.
Classification: LCC PZ7.1.F48 Cra 2019(print)
LC record available at https://lccn.loc.gov/2019940825

1

"What's that noise?"

2

"It's coming from inside that plastic bag."

 3

"It's a baby bird tangled in a plastic bag."
Pedro said.

4

"I'm Homer. I'm stuck. Help!"

"How can we help him?"

"I know," Anna said,
"Try flapping your wings really fast."

"It's no good. He's still stuck."
said Luna.

 8

"Try twisting your way free,"
Sanjay said.

9

"I'm more tangled now.
What's your next big idea?"

10

"I've got it! I'll bite the plastic off,"
Homer said.

"NO! If you swallow that you'll get sick.

"So, what can we do?"

"Lets get Dad,"
Luna said.

Luna's dad knew just what to do.

He listened carefully to their instructions.

"Luna, please get a towel. I'll get a ladder and...

SCISSORS!"

"Don't be afraid, Homer. Dad will cut you free."

And that's just what dad did.

 20

"Homer's free! He's free!"

Luna and her friends were happy.

They walked to the playground.

Luna could not believe her eyes.

25

"What can we do to stop this?"

"What can we **all** do?"

# "What Can We Do to Stop This?

Here are some ideas we can do to help our animal friends.
Can you think of any others?

- Use trash cans to throw away your garbage
- Throw away plastic items in a special recycle bin
  These items might hurt animals and will be made into something
   else that is safe. You have one where you live
- Make a poster of things that can be recycled,
  Some of these things are:
    - Plastic bags
    - Plastic baskets and toys
    - Newspapers
    - Cereal boxes
    - Metal cans
    - Glass bottles
- Ask your parents and grocer to use reusable bags
- Don't ask for straws
- Get your class to adopt a part of your playground for cleaning up
- Have your class put on a play about things that can hurt animals
  and what we can do to help
- Don't buy toys made out of plastic

# What would you do if you saw an animal in trouble? Who would you call?

_____

_____

_____

_____

_____

_____

DRAW
AND COLOR
LUNA AND HOMER

Paula Feuerstein has a Master's degree in Elementary Education and a Ph.D. in Curriculum Development. Paula is passionate about helping children learn. She has taught elementary school students in public and private schools in New York and Illinois and developed educational books and learning experiences that have won state and national awards.

Paula is a strong advocate of helping children learn about the environment. She is married and has two children (who she's loved sharing her love for the environment with).

## Other works by Paula Feuerstein
- *You're Going to Mars: Time to Make a Spacesuit*
- *How to Build a Museum Exhibit for a Kachina doll*
- *Westward Bound*
- *How to Look Up Words in the Dictionary*
- *Create Your Own Make Believe Character*

Made in the
USA
Columbia, SC